VIKING

Published by the Penguin Group
Penguin Books Ltd, 27 Wrights Lane, London W8 5TZ,
England
Penguin Putnam Inc., 375 Hudson Street, New York, New
York 10014, USA
Penguin Books Australia Ltd, Ringwood, Victoria, Australia
Penguin Books Canada Ltd, 10 Alcorn Avenue, Toronto,
Ontario, Canada M4V 3B2
Penguin Books India (P) Ltd, 11 Community Centre,
Panchsheel Park, New Delhi – 110 017, India
Penguin Books (NZ) Ltd, Cnr Rosedale and Airborne
Roads, Albany, Auckland, New Zealand
Penguin Books (South Africa) (Pty) Ltd, 5 Watkins Street,
Denver Ext 4, Johannesburg 2094, South Africa

On the World Wide Web at: www.penguin.com

Penguin Books Ltd, Registered Offices: Harmondsworth,
Middlesex, England

First published 2001
1 3 5 7 9 10 8 6 4 2

Set in 10pt Chicago

Printed in Italy by L. E. G. O.

British Library Cataloguing in Publication Data
A CIP catalogue record for this book is available from the
British Library

ISBN 0670–91176–3

CONTENTS

TEXTING, TEXTING, 1, 2, 3 . . .

Why do we love text messaging? Because it keeps conversations short, sweet and simple. You can swap opinions, send jokes, make last-minute plans and get down to some serious gossip — all by text alone. And no one can listen in.

So get this book, grab that mobile and go text!

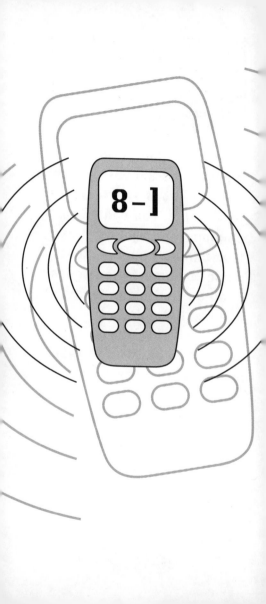

CHEEKY CHAT

Stuck for words?
Look no further.

BBIW
Big Brother is watching

BEG
Big evil grin

BMGWL
Busting my gut with laughter

BWL
Bursting with laughter

C&G
Chuckle and grin

CRBT
Crying real big tears

CSG
Chuckle snigger grin

CULA
See you later alligator
(see L8R G8R)

DLTBBB
Don't let the bed bugs bite

DOS
Dozing off soon

DTB
Don't text back

FC
Fingers crossed

FTBOMH
From the bottom of my heart

GFN
Going for now

GMAB
Give me a break

GOOMF
Get out of my face

GTSY
Glad/Good to see you

HAG1
Have a good one

HHOK
Ha ha only kidding

HIG
How's it going?

HT
Hi there

IAWC
In a while crocodile

IBTD
I beg to differ

ITIGBS
I think I'm gonna
be sick

IWIST
I wish I'd said that

IYKWIM
If you know what I mean

J4G
Just for grins

JK
Just kidding

JMO
Just my opinion

JWTK
Just want to know

KYFC
Keep your fingers crossed

L8R G8R
Later 'gator (see CULA)

LMHO
Laughing my head off

LSHMBB
Laughing so hard my belly's bouncing

LSHMBH
Laughing so hard my belly hurts

LTS
Laughing to self

MTF
More to follow

MTFBWY
May the force be with you

NIMBY
Not in my back yard

NP
No problem

NTW
Not to worry

PDS
Please don't shoot

PMFJI
Pardon me for jumping in

Rents r abt
My parents are about/around

ROFL
Rolling on floor laughing

ROFLUTS
Rolling on floor laughing
unable to speak

ROFLWTIME
Rolling on floor laughing with
tears in my eyes

RSN
Real soon now

RT
Real time

RUTHERE
Are you there?

Sup?
What's up?

:X
Secret's safe with me

SETE
Smiling ear to ear

SHID
Slaps head in disgust

SICS
Sitting in chair sniggering

SITD
Still in the dark

SOT
Short of time

SOTMG
Short of time must go

SPAM
Stupid persons' advertisement

SWIM
See what I mean

SWL
Screaming with laughter

TCOY
Take care of yourself

VEG
Very evil grin

VWD
Very well done

Wan2tlk
Want to talk?

WB
Welcome back

WDYT
What do you think?

WEG
Wicked evil grin

WIBAMU
Well I'll be a monkey's uncle

Wot 4
What for?

WTG
Way to go!

WUD
What you/What are you doing?

YBS
You'll be sorry

YIU
Yes I understand

YSW
Yeah sure whatever

YSWUS
Yeah sure whatever you say

UTLKIN2ME
(Are) you talking to me?

_!
Enough for now

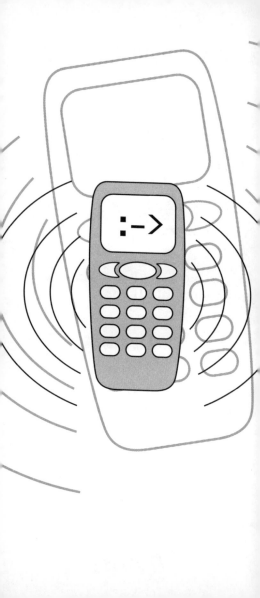

SO SMILEY

Smileys (aka Emoticons) are little sideways faces that tell people exactly how you're feeling. So let it all out and send someone a Smiley today.

RAPID REACTIONS

:l	Hmmm?
8-]	Wow man!
:-o	Oh Oh!
:-*	Ooops!
:@	Ouch!
(8-o	Who is that?
:^D"	Great! I like it

| `^5` | High five |

| `8-)` | Eyes wide with surprise |

OH SO TIRED

| `%-)` | Staring at screen for too long |

| `:-0` | Yawning |

| `:-6` | Exhausted |

| `I-I` | Asleep |

| `I-0` | Snoring |

| `%-6` | Braindead |

| `x-(` | Dead |

SMILEY HAPPY PEOPLE

`;-D` **Friendly, winking**

`{8-}` **Grinning**

`I-D` **Ho Ho!**

`:- ) :- ) :- )` **Loud guffaw**

`:-y` **Said with a smile**

`(-_-)` **Secret smile**

`0 8-)` **Feeling angelic/innocent**

NOT QUITE SO HAPPY

`\-o` **Bored**

`:-I` **Not bothered**

Emoticon	Meaning
:-I	Indifferent
:->	Sarcastic
>:->	Devilish
>;->	Devilish but playful
:o(	Sad with a big nose
:'-)	Crying with laughter
:'-(	Crying sadly
(:-&	Angry
(>õ<)	Furious
**-(	Too many shocks

USER FRIENDLY

`:-~(`   User has a cold

`:-#`   User has a brace

`(-:`   Left-handed user

HEADCASES

`B-)`   Wearing sunglasses

`B:-)`   Sunglasses on head

`:U:-I`   Alligator on head

`[:-)`   Wearing a walkman

ME, ME, ME

(@-@) I am stunned

(0-0) I am shocked

(*-*) I am in love

(>-<) I am furious

{{(>-<)}} I am freezing

(0υ0) I am a night owl

HAIR NECESSITIES

~#:- (Bad hair day

-:-) Hair in a mohawk

r:-) Hair in a ponytail

| `8:-)` | Hair is curly |
| `{:-)` | Hair is parted in the middle |

SNACK ATTACK

`:-*`	Sour taste
`:-9`	Delicious / Licking my lips
`:-)~`	Drooling
`****`	Popcorn
`8888`	Pretzels
`:-))`	Double chin

VIRTUAL ZOO

`:=8`	**Baboon**
`^-^`	**Bat**
`~o~`	**Bird**
`}:-<`	**Cat**
`8^`	**Chicken**
`3:-o`	**Cow**
`:3-<`	**Dog**
`6U)`	**Elephant**
`>-^);>`	**Fish**
`8)`	**Frog**
`8:]`	**Gorilla**

:8)	Pig
====:	Snake
====:[	Snake with fangs

NOSEY PARKER

:>)	Nose, big
:c)	Nose, wide
:^(	Broken nose
:v)	Broken nose the other way
:_)	Nose is sliding off face
:=)	Two noses
:+(	Punched nose, hurt

GET A JOB

:-%	Banker
d:-)	Baseball player
8=:-)	Chef
*<:o)	Clown
*<:o)X	Clown with bow tie
=:-H	Football player
[:]	Robot
<8 :-)	Wizard
=:-)	Punk rocker
=:-(	Real punk rockers don't smile

BUFFY'S M8S

`:-[`   Vampire

`:-E`   Buck-toothed vampire

`:-F`   Buck-toothed vampire with one tooth missing

STAR WARS

`(-o-)`   Star Wars Tie Fighter

`>o<`   Star Wars X wing

NASTY NAMES

(:I   Egghead

<:-)   Dunce

:---)   Liar

:-------) Big, big liar

HI-BROW

',;-)   Raising an eyebrow

':-)   Shaved off an
           eyebrow

,:-)   Shaved off the other
           eyebrow

TUMMY TROUBLE

:-) .	**Belly button innie**
:-) ,	**Belly button outie**

CHATTERBOXES

:-( )	**Talk a lot**
(:<)	**Blabbermouth**
:-X	**Lips are sealed**

PETPALS

3:]	**Pet smiley**
3:[	**Unhappy pet smiley**

EYE EYE

`.-)`   One eye

`,-)`   One eye winking

`'-)`   The other eye winking

SICK DAY

`(:():)`   Plaster/Band-Aid

THE SIMPSONS

`(_8^(I)`   Homer

`@@@@:-)`   Marge

MIDGET SMILEYS

Quickies for when you're SOT (short of time)

`:)`   Smile

`:]`   Grin

`:D`   Laughter

`:(`   Sad

`:[`   Very unhappy

`:O`   Yelling

`:,(`   Crying

`II`   Asleep

LUV YA

Just text to say 'I love you'

B my ~:@   Be my baby

CW2CU   Can't wait to see you

HOLLAND   Hoping our love lasts and never dies

IWALU   I will always love you

KIT   Keep in touch

KOC   Kiss on cheek

LUWAMH   Love you with all my heart

LY **LUVYA**	Love you
LY2	Love you too
QT	Cutie
SNTW/A:-*	Sent with a kiss
SUM1luvsU	Someone loves you
SWALK	Sealed with a loving kiss
SYS	See you soon
TOY	Thinking of you
URAQT	You are a cutie
WAS	What a sweetie
(()):*	Hugs and kisses

XOXOXO	Hugs and kisses
:*	Kiss
((((name))))	Hug
G	Giggle
H	Hug
K	Kiss
W	Wink
<3<3<3	Hearts
:#)	Blushing
:-&	Shy
:-{}	Blowing a kiss

Y not send a little xtra sumthg??

Roses r red
Violets r blue
U 4 me
& me 4 U

Roses r red
Violets r blue
I wan 2 txt
My luv 2 U

We go 2gether like
(_8^(I)
and
@@@@:-)

(See The Simpsons page 28)

RINGING
RHYMES

Phone with a poem today

Not getting an answer? Try this

> NE1 there?
> NE1 home?
> Got no1 2 tlk 2
> Pls pick up ur phone

Kept waiting again?

> UR funny
> UR gr8
> Xept when U R always L8

And if you're the late one ...

> Just wan2 say
> I'm a lil l8
> B4 you get mad
> Let me say sry m8

Desperate to talk?

> Here I am
> By the phone
> Pls call me
> I'm all alone

Send this to a know-all m8

2Ys U R
2Ys U B
I C U R
2 Ys 4 me

**Songs for a special day –
choose your version**

Hpy brthdy 2 U
Hpy brthdy 2 U
UR sum1 special
& a gr8 m8 2

Hpy brthdy 2 U (x 2)
Sry its L8
Da best I c%d do

Hpy brthdy 2 U (x 2)
U look like a 8:)
Tht I saw at the zoo

MOANING MINNIES

Go on, get it off your chest ...

APU
As per usual

CID
Crying in disgrace

CSY
Can't stop yawning

DIY
Do it yourself

GASP
Go away silly person

HHIS
Hanging head in shame

IH8
I hate ...

INV
I envy ...

KHYF
Know how you feel

MBR$D
Embarrassed

NETUA
No one ever tells us anything

NM
Nightmare!

OMG
Oh my god!

PPP
Petty pet peeve

TSR
Totally stupid rules

URT wkst lnk gbye
**You are the weakest
link goodbye**

Wot a dogz dnr
What a dog's dinner

WOTAM
Waste of time and money

:-c
Little sulk

:-C
Big sulk

WISE WORDS

Take our advice and read on

DJST
Don't just sit there

DSO
Don't stress out

FME
Follow my example

IIABDFI
If it ain't broke, don't fix it

IIWM
If it were me ...

ITSFWI
If the shoe fits, wear it

KIR
Keep it real

KYHD
Keep your head down

Liv ur drm
Live your dream

Luvs all u nd
Love is all you need

POAHF
Put on a happy face

:-$
Put your money where your mouth is

SCCC
Stay cool, calm, collected

YGWYPF
You get what you pay for

JUST 4 FUN!

Get your m8s falling off their chairs laughing ...

(Have you heard the one about ... ?)

HUHT1 abt 3 holes in the grnd?

No? Well, well, well

HUHT1 abt 3 eggs?

No? 2 bad

HUHT1 abt the pony wiva cough?

It's a lil hoarse

HUHT1 abt the hitch-hiker?

Way 2 go

HUHT1 abt the golfer's sox?

He got a hole in 1

Wadya get if u dial 76503847756335241049584837389?

Blister on UR fnger

Wadya call a rapper wiva cold?

Phlegm-inem

Wadya call a rapper in a strop?

Huff Daddy

Wadya call a gorilla wiva gun?

Sir

Y did the man throw his watch out the window?

2 C time fly

Wadya call frozen water?

Ice

Wadya call frozen tea?

Iced tea

Wadya call frozen ink?

Iced ink

U SMELL!!!

Spell a hungry horse in 4 letters.

MTGG

Wadya get if u x a horse wiva mobile?

Neigh as u go

Wadya get if u x Homer Simpson wiva mobile?

Pay as u DOH!

Wadya get if U x a Teletubby wiva mobile?

Pay as u Po

Wadya get if u x Santa wiva mobile?

Pay as you ho, ho, ho

Wadya get if u x a witch wivan ice cube?

A cold spell

Wadya get if u x a spell wiva snake?

Abra da cobra

Wadya get if u x an elephant wiva fish?

Swimming trunks

Wadya get if u x a cow wiva gr8 school report?

Big pat on the back

Wot goes ZZUB ZZUB?

A B flying BWDS

Wot goes 99 clump, 99 clump?

Centipede wiva broken leg

Wot goes ha, ha, ha, OW?

Sum1 FOTFL

Wot is a cat's fvrte dnr?

Egg fried mice

Wadya call a deer wiv no eyes?

No idea

Y did the hedgehog x the rd?

2 C his flat m8

Y is 6 scared of 7?

Cos 7 8 9

Y R N and O so important?

Cos you can't get ON w/out them

Wot's a wok?

Wot u throw at a wabbit when u haven't gotta wifle

Wot's a twip?

Wot a wabbit calls a twain wide

Wadya call a man in the C?

Bob

Wadya call a woman who gets up ur nose?

Vicks

Wot's grey & white & red all over?

An MBR$D elephant

FUNEX?
IFNNEX - 18M!

(Get it? Have you any eggs? I haven't any eggs - I ate 'em!)

Want to come back on a joke?
Here are a few ideas:

:/	Not funny
:-D	Laughing
FOTFL	Falling on the floor laughing
HHVF	Ha ha very funny
IDGI	I don't get it
LMHO	Laughing my head off
LSHMBB	Laughing so hard my belly's bouncing
LSHMBH	Laughing so hard my belly hurts
ONNA	Oh no, not again

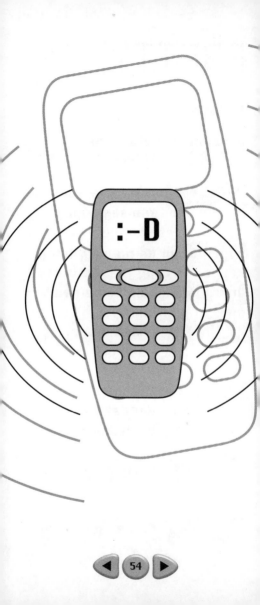

PRETTY PIX

Who needs words when pictures say it all?

(Note: You will need a Nokia mobile phone to send and receive these images. Use the punctuation marks on your keypad to copy the pictures. Or try making up some new ones of your own.)

Toothy grin

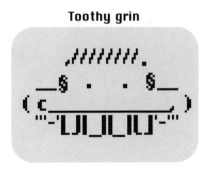

Bear hug

```
----@''''''''@----
    ''|_|''
-----( - )-----
---(#)ILuvU(#)---
-----(#)   (#)-----
```

```
----@''''''''@----
    ''|_|''
-----( - )-----
(#)This  Much(#)
----(#)   (#)----
```

Here kitty, kitty

```
()" "()()" "()
( ='o'= ) ( ='o'= )
-(,,)-(,,)-(,,)-(,,)-
```

Flirty frog

```
(o)(o)  (o)(-)
 (_)     (_)
(,,)--(,,)(,,)--(,,)
```

Disco ant

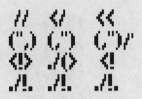

Puppy pal

Chatty chums

Triumphant ted

BACK TO BASICS

Messaging maniacs know that anything goes in the world of texting. All you have to do is make everything as short and simple as possible. Use letters instead of words (RU = Are You ...?), make sentences into groups of letters (BCNU!) and spell words however you like. It's fun and it saves your fingers from getting tired!

Look over the page for some text basics you might need reminding of.

2	To/too/two
4	For
A?	Eh?
@	At
B	Be
B4	Before
B/C	Because
Bezzie	Best mate
C	See/sea
C%D	Could
Coz	Because
Da	The

Ez	Easy
F2T	Free to talk?
Gonna	Going to
IC	I see
IK	I know
L8	Late
Lil	Little
M8	Mate
MOB	Mobile
MSG	Message
NE	Any
NE1	Anyone

Nethng	Anything
NO1	No one
OK	Okay
Pls	Please
R	Are
Rents	Parents
S%D	Should
SEC	Wait a second
Spk	Speak
SOS	Help!
Soz	Sorry
Sry	Sorry

SUM1	Someone
Ta	Thanks
Tho	Though
THX	Thanks
TYVM	Thank you very much
U	You
UR	Your/You're
W/	With
W%D	Would
Wan2	Want to
WKND	Weekend

W/O Without

W8 Wait

Zzzzzz Very bored/asleep

INDEX

```
(|><)}}}*<:o)X<3<3<3*G*TOYXOXOXO
&&&:-)~(@-@)B:-):- ) :- ) :-
-):]~:@MBR$D%-){{{(><)}}*<:o)
<) 3:[(-o-)3:-o}:-<&&&&:-)~(@
8 B 4 B = = = =:[ m y ( _ 8 ^
|><)}}}*<:o)X<3<3<3*G*TOYXOXO
&&&:-)~(@-@)B:-):- ) :-
m y(_ 8 ^ ( | )<8:-):]~:@ M
*G*TOYXOXOXO:0:^(@@@@:-)(:<
) :- ) :- ) (-__)(>õ<):->
$D%-){{{(><)}}*<:o)X<3<3<3*G*T
:-o}:-<&&&&:-)~(@-@)B:-
:o)X<3<3<3*G*TOYXOXOXO:0:^(
( @ - @ ) B : - ) : - ) : - ) (
*<:o)X<3<3<3*G*TOYXOXOXO:0:
õ<)>:->L 8 B 4 B = = = =:[ m y
|><)}}}*<:o)X<3<3<3*G*TOYXOXO
&&&:-)~(@-@)B:-):- ) :- ) :-
-):]~:@MBR$D%-){{{(><)}}*<:o)
) 3:[(-o-)3:-o}:-<&&&&:-)~(@
8 B 4 B = = = = : [ m y ( _ 8 ^
|><)}}}*<:o)X<3<3<3*G*TOYXOXO
&&&:-)~(@-@)B:-):-):-
n y(_ 8 ^ ( | )<8:-):]~:@ M
*G*TOYXOXOXO:0:^(@@@@:-)(:<
):-):-)(-__)(>õ<):->L 8 B 4
$D%-){{{(><)}}*<:o)X<3<3<3*G*T
-o}:-<&&&&:-)~(@-@)B:-
:o)X<3<3<3*G*TOYXOXOXO:0:^(
( @ - @ ) B : - ) : - ) : - ) :
*<:o)X<3<3<3*G*TOYXOXOXO
&&(>õ<)>:->L 8 B 4 B = = = =:[
|><)}}}*<:o)X<3<3<3*G*TOYXOXO
&&&:-)~(@-@)B:-):- ) :- ) :-
-):]~:@MBR$D%-){{{(><)}}*<:o)
<)3:[(-o-)3:-o}:-<&&&&:-)]
```